The Busy Author's
Book Marketing
Journal

An Action Guide for Authors

Vibrant Marketing Publications
Hartford, CT

Published by Vibrant Marketing Publications
Copyright ©2016 D'vorah Lansky

www.ActionGuidesForAuthors.com

ISBN 978-0-9967431-3-6

Dedication

This journal is dedicated to the amazing, success-focused authors and guest experts who've participated in our book marketing courses and conferences over the years!

It is a joy to be on this journey with you!

Notes

How to Use This Journal

Once you've written and published your book, it's essential to do something, each day, to market your books. You can accomplish a great deal even in a few minutes a day! This will help you gain momentum and will increase your visibility exponentially!

To help you keep on track, schedule a recurring appointment in your calendar each day, for the next 30 days. This will serve as a reminder and will help you to prioritize your book marketing efforts.

Based on your schedule and lifestyle, you decide whether you'll be marketing your book five, six, or seven days a week.

By focusing on marketing your book on a regular and ongoing basis, you will get your book in front of the exact people who could benefit from your message.

Turn the page and scan through the collection of book marketing strategies and ideas. Draw from these, as you choose your daily book marketing activities. Additionally, be sure to draw from other book marketing strategies that you are aware of.

Get ready to have fun, sell more books, and enjoy the opportunities that will come your way as a result of your efforts.

Here's to Your Success!

Book Marketing Activities

Always be ready to share your passion about your book, not in a salesy way, but in an informative way.

Blog about your book or topic at least once a week.

Contact blog owners who write on topics related to yours and arrange to be a guest blogger.

Deliver great content when speaking or writing about your book or topic.

Email your list of subscribers at least once a week and share a tip from your book.

Find author groups in your geographical area.

Guest speak on teleseminars and podcasts.

Host guest speakers who speak or write on topics of interest to your audience.

Include testimonials in your email newsletter.

Join author networking groups online and offline.

Kindle relationships with leaders in your field.

Listen to podcasts in your topic area and reach out to the host and ask to be a guest on their show.

Make marketing fun by planning activities such as online book launch parties.

Book Marketing Activities

Network in your local area as well as in online groups that attract your target audience.

Order business cards that list your book title and web address. Pass them out at networking events.

Prepare a series of questions about your author journey and your book, to prepare for interviews.

Quiz book stores to see if they host book talks.

Request reviews and testimonials, each and every time someone tells you they enjoy your book.

Sell your books at local fairs.

Talk about your book and your author journey, to television show hosts in your local area.

Use testimonials and reviews on your website.

Volunteer as a guest speaker at your local library, chamber of commerce, or author's group.

Watch for speaking and writing opportunities.

eXamine your book marketing plan and identify any unrealized marketing opportunities.

Yellow line openings in your calendar where you can spend a few minutes marketing your book.

Zealously continue to market your book.

Notes

Notes

Day 1

What I Did to Market My Book

_____

_____

_____

_____

_____

_____

What I Am Grateful For

_____

_____

_____

_____

_____

Date: _____

Tactics That Are Working

_____

_____

_____

_____

_____

_____

Results I Am Experiencing

_____

_____

_____

_____

_____

_____

Day 2

What I Did to Market My Book

_____

_____

_____

_____

_____

_____

What I Am Grateful For

_____

_____

_____

_____

_____

Date: _____

Tactics That Are Working

_____

_____

_____

_____

_____

_____

Results I Am Experiencing

_____

_____

_____

_____

_____

Day 3

What I Did to Market My Book

_____

_____

_____

_____

_____

_____

What I Am Grateful For

_____

_____

_____

_____

_____

_____

Date: _____

Tactics That Are Working

_____

_____

_____

_____

_____

_____

Results I Am Experiencing

_____

_____

_____

_____

_____

Day 4

What I Did to Market My Book

_____

_____

_____

_____

_____

What I Am Grateful For

_____

_____

_____

_____

_____

$\mathcal{D}$ate: _____

Tactics That Are Working

_____

_____

_____

_____

_____

_____

Results I Am Experiencing

_____

_____

_____

_____

_____

Day 5

What I Did to Market My Book

_____

_____

_____

_____

_____

What I Am Grateful For

_____

_____

_____

_____

_____

Date: _____

Tactics That Are Working

_____

_____

_____

_____

_____

Results I Am Experiencing

_____

_____

_____

_____

_____

Day 6

What I Did to Market My Book

_____

_____

_____

_____

_____

_____

What I Am Grateful For

_____

_____

_____

_____

_____

_____

Date: _____

Tactics That Are Working

_____

_____

_____

_____

_____

_____

Results I Am Experiencing

_____

_____

_____

_____

_____

_____

Day 7

What I Did to Market My Book

_____
_____
_____
_____
_____
_____

What I Am Grateful For

_____
_____
_____
_____
_____
_____

Date: _____

Tactics That Are Working

_____

_____

_____

_____

_____

_____

Results I Am Experiencing

_____

_____

_____

_____

_____

Day 8

What I Did to Market My Book

_____

_____

_____

_____

_____

_____

What I Am Grateful For

_____

_____

_____

_____

_____

Date: _____

Tactics That Are Working

_____

_____

_____

_____

_____

_____

Results I Am Experiencing

_____

_____

_____

_____

_____

Day 9

What I Did to Market My Book

_____

_____

_____

_____

_____

_____

What I Am Grateful For

_____

_____

_____

_____

_____

_____

Date: _____

Tactics That Are Working

_____

_____

_____

_____

_____

_____

Results I Am Experiencing

_____

_____

_____

_____

_____

$\mathcal{D}$ay 10

What I Did to Market My Book

_____

_____

_____

_____

_____

_____

What I Am Grateful For

_____

_____

_____

_____

_____

Date: _____

Tactics That Are Working

_____

_____

_____

_____

_____

_____

Results I Am Experiencing

_____

_____

_____

_____

_____

Day 11

What I Did to Market My Book

_____

_____

_____

_____

_____

_____

What I Am Grateful For

_____

_____

_____

_____

_____

_____

Date: _____

Tactics That Are Working

_____

_____

_____

_____

_____

_____

Results I Am Experiencing

_____

_____

_____

_____

_____

Day 12

What I Did to Market My Book

_____

_____

_____

_____

_____

_____

What I Am Grateful For

_____

_____

_____

_____

_____

Date: _____

Tactics That Are Working

_____

_____

_____

_____

_____

_____

Results I Am Experiencing

_____

_____

_____

_____

_____

Day 13

What I Did to Market My Book

_____

_____

_____

_____

_____

_____

What I Am Grateful For

_____

_____

_____

_____

_____

_____

Date: _____

Tactics That Are Working

_____

_____

_____

_____

_____

_____

Results I Am Experiencing

_____

_____

_____

_____

_____

Day 14

What I Did to Market My Book

_____

_____

_____

_____

_____

_____

What I Am Grateful For

_____

_____

_____

_____

_____

_____

Date: _____

Tactics That Are Working

_____

_____

_____

_____

_____

_____

Results I Am Experiencing

_____

_____

_____

_____

_____

Day 15

What I Did to Market My Book

_____

_____

_____

_____

_____

What I Am Grateful For

_____

_____

_____

_____

_____

Date: _____

Tactics That Are Working

_____
_____
_____
_____
_____
_____

Results I Am Experiencing

_____
_____
_____
_____
_____
_____

Day 16

What I Did to Market My Book

_____

_____

_____

_____

_____

_____

What I Am Grateful For

_____

_____

_____

_____

_____

_____

Date: _____

Tactics That Are Working

_____

_____

_____

_____

_____

Results I Am Experiencing

_____

_____

_____

_____

_____

Day 17

What I Did to Market My Book

_____

_____

_____

_____

_____

_____

What I Am Grateful For

_____

_____

_____

_____

_____

_____

Date: _____

Tactics That Are Working

_____

_____

_____

_____

_____

Results I Am Experiencing

_____

_____

_____

_____

_____

Day 18

What I Did to Market My Book

_____

_____

_____

_____

_____

_____

What I Am Grateful For

_____

_____

_____

_____

_____

_____

Date: _____

Tactics That Are Working

_____

_____

_____

_____

_____

_____

Results I Am Experiencing

_____

_____

_____

_____

_____

Day 19

What I Did to Market My Book

_____

_____

_____

_____

_____

What I Am Grateful For

_____

_____

_____

_____

_____

Date: _____

Tactics That Are Working

_____

_____

_____

_____

_____

_____

Results I Am Experiencing

_____

_____

_____

_____

_____

_____

$\mathcal{D}ay$ 20

What I Did to Market My Book

_____

_____

_____

_____

_____

What I Am Grateful For

_____

_____

_____

_____

_____

Date: _____

Tactics That Are Working

_____
_____
_____
_____
_____
_____

Results I Am Experiencing

_____
_____
_____
_____
_____

Day 21

What I Did to Market My Book

_____

_____

_____

_____

_____

What I Am Grateful For

_____

_____

_____

_____

_____

Date: _____

Tactics That Are Working

_____

_____

_____

_____

_____

_____

Results I Am Experiencing

_____

_____

_____

_____

_____

_____

Day 22

What I Did to Market My Book

_____

_____

_____

_____

_____

_____

What I Am Grateful For

_____

_____

_____

_____

_____

Date: _____

Tactics That Are Working

_____

_____

_____

_____

_____

_____

Results I Am Experiencing

_____

_____

_____

_____

_____

Day 23

What I Did to Market My Book

_____

_____

_____

_____

_____

What I Am Grateful For

_____

_____

_____

_____

_____

Date: _____

Tactics That Are Working

_____

_____

_____

_____

_____

_____

Results I Am Experiencing

_____

_____

_____

_____

_____

_____

Day 24

What I Did to Market My Book

_____

_____

_____

_____

_____

_____

What I Am Grateful For

_____

_____

_____

_____

_____

Date: _____

Tactics That Are Working

_____

_____

_____

_____

_____

Results I Am Experiencing

_____

_____

_____

_____

_____

$\mathcal{D}$ay 25

What I Did to Market My Book

_____
_____
_____
_____
_____
_____

What I Am Grateful For

_____
_____
_____
_____
_____
_____

Date: _____

Tactics That Are Working

_____

_____

_____

_____

_____

_____

Results I Am Experiencing

_____

_____

_____

_____

_____

$\mathcal{D}$ay 26

What I Did to Market My Book

_____

_____

_____

_____

_____

_____

What I Am Grateful For

_____

_____

_____

_____

_____

Date: _____

Tactics That Are Working

_____

_____

_____

_____

_____

_____

Results I Am Experiencing

_____

_____

_____

_____

_____

Day 27

What I Did to Market My Book

_____

_____

_____

_____

_____

_____

What I Am Grateful For

_____

_____

_____

_____

_____

_____

Date: _____

Tactics That Are Working

_____

_____

_____

_____

_____

_____

Results I Am Experiencing

_____

_____

_____

_____

_____

_____

Day 28

What I Did to Market My Book

_____

_____

_____

_____

_____

_____

What I Am Grateful For

_____

_____

_____

_____

_____

_____

Date: _____

Tactics That Are Working

_____

_____

_____

_____

_____

Results I Am Experiencing

_____

_____

_____

_____

_____

$\mathcal{D}$ay 29

What I Did to Market My Book

_____

_____

_____

_____

_____

_____

What I Am Grateful For

_____

_____

_____

_____

_____

_____

Date: _____

Tactics That Are Working

_____

_____

_____

_____

_____

_____

Results I Am Experiencing

_____

_____

_____

_____

_____

Day 30

What I Did to Market My Book

_____

_____

_____

_____

_____

What I Am Grateful For

_____

_____

_____

_____

_____

Date: _____

Tactics That Are Working

_____

_____

_____

_____

_____

Results I Am Experiencing

_____

_____

_____

_____

_____

Notes

Notes

Notes

_____
_____
_____
_____
_____
_____
_____
_____
_____
_____
_____
_____
_____
_____
_____
_____
_____

Resource
Pages

Authors Who Write Books on Topics of Interest to My Readers

Name: _____

Book Title: _____

Website: _____

Name: _____

Book Title: _____

Website: _____

Name: _____

Book Title: _____

Website: _____

Name: _____

Book Title: _____

Website: _____

Name: _____

Book Title: _____

Website: _____

Authors Who Write Books on Topics of Interest to My Readers

Name: _____

Book Title: _____

Website: _____

Name: _____

Book Title: _____

Website: _____

Name: _____

Book Title: _____

Website: _____

Name: _____

Book Title: _____

Website: _____

Name: _____

Book Title: _____

Website: _____

Blogs on Topics of Interest to My Readers

Blog Owner: _____

Name of Blog: _____

URL: _____

Blog Owner: _____

Name of Blog: _____

URL: _____

Blog Owner: _____

Name of Blog: _____

URL: _____

Blog Owner: _____

Name of Blog: _____

URL: _____

Blog Owner: _____

Name of Blog: _____

URL: _____

Blogs on Topics of Interest to My Readers

Blog Owner: _____

Name of Blog: _____

URL: _____

Blog Owner: _____

Name of Blog: _____

URL: _____

Blog Owner: _____

Name of Blog: _____

URL: _____

Blog Owner: _____

Name of Blog: _____

URL: _____

Blog Owner: _____

Name of Blog: _____

URL: _____

Things to Blog About

If you are knowledgeable and passionate about the topic of your book, it's likely that you have a lot to say. Creating a variety of blog posts will keep your audience interested and coming back for more.

Following is a list of ideas to draw from, when writing posts for your blog or witing as a guest blogger for other blogs.

- ☐ Write about the message behind your book.
- ☐ Share content or excerpts from your book.
- ☐ Talk about your author journey.
- ☐ Share an update about a recent book reading or interview you've participated in.
- ☐ Tell how you came to write your book.
- ☐ Write a post based on an idea inspired by a comment from a reader of your blog.
- ☐ Comment on a news event and how it relates to your topic.
- ☐ Write a how-to post.
- ☐ Answer a common question on your topic.
- ☐ Create a series of posts such as "The Top 10 Ways To…" or "7 Tips For…"

Things to Blog About

- ☐ Tell an entertaining and educational story, related to your topic.
- ☐ Address common frustrations in your industry.
- ☐ Compose a step-by-step tutorial on something of interest to your readers.
- ☐ Make a list of commonly asked questions on your topic and share your answers.
- ☐ Collect questions from your audience and answer one question per post.

For Fiction Authors

- ☐ Revise the ideas listed above and on the previous page so they apply to your book.
- ☐ Tell the back story of your characters.
- ☐ Feature a different character in each post.
- ☐ Interview your characters and take your readers on an adventure.
- ☐ Have your characters interview you.
- ☐ Have characters interview one another.
- ☐ Turn the page and continue to list ideas of things to blog about.

Idea for a Blog Post

_____

_____

_____

_____

_____

_____

_____

Idea for a Blog Post

_____

_____

_____

_____

_____

_____

_____

More Things to Blog About

Podcasts & Radio Shows
of Interest to My Readers

Host Name: _____
Show Name: _____
Show URL: _____

Host Name: _____
Show Name: _____
Show URL: _____

Host Name: _____
Show Name: _____
Show URL: _____

Host Name: _____
Show Name: _____
Show URL: _____

Host Name: _____
Show Name: _____
Show URL: _____

Podcasts & Radio Shows
of Interest to My Readers

Host Name: _____
Show Name: _____
Show URL: _____

Host Name: _____
Show Name: _____
Show URL: _____

Host Name: _____
Show Name: _____
Show URL: _____

Host Name: _____
Show Name: _____
Show URL: _____

Host Name: _____
Show Name: _____
Show URL: _____

Keeping Track of My
Speaking Engagements

Name of Host: _____

Host's Website: _____

Date of Interview: _____

Topic of Interview: _____

Notes: _____

Name of Host: _____

Host's Website: _____

Date of Interview: _____

Topic of Interview: _____

Notes: _____

Name of Host: _____

Host's Website: _____

Date of Interview: _____

Topic of Interview: _____

Notes: _____

Keeping Track of My Speaking Engagements

Name of Host: _____

Host's Website: _____

Date of Interview: _____

Topic of Interview: _____

Notes: _____

Name of Host: _____

Host's Website: _____

Date of Interview: _____

Topic of Interview: _____

Notes: _____

Name of Host: _____

Host's Website: _____

Date of Interview: _____

Topic of Interview: _____

Notes: _____

Keeping Track of My Speaking Engagements

Name of Host: _____

Host's Website: _____

Date of Interview: _____

Topic of Interview: _____

Notes: _____

Name of Host: _____

Host's Website: _____

Date of Interview: _____

Topic of Interview: _____

Notes: _____

Name of Host: _____

Host's Website: _____

Date of Interview: _____

Topic of Interview: _____

Notes: _____

Keeping Track of My Speaking Engagements

Name of Host: _____

Host's Website: _____

Date of Interview: _____

Topic of Interview: _____

Notes: _____

Name of Host: _____

Host's Website: _____

Date of Interview: _____

Topic of Interview: _____

Notes: _____

Name of Host: _____

Host's Website: _____

Date of Interview: _____

Topic of Interview: _____

Notes: _____

Notes

Notes

_____

_____

_____

_____

_____

_____

_____

_____

_____

_____

_____

_____

_____

_____

_____

_____

_____

_____

About D'vorah

D'vorah Lansky, M.Ed. is the bestselling author of several books including; *Book Marketing Made Easy: Simple Strategies for Selling Your Nonfiction Book Online*.

Since 2006 D'vorah has created more than 25, successful, online programs and has taught and coached thousands of authors across the globe.

D'vorah has spoken on over 500 teleseminars and podcasts, and has helped many authors develop their own podcasts and teleseminar series.

She specializes in teaching authors how to reach more readers and sell more books, using online book marketing strategies.

To view all of D'vorah's books visit her on Amazon at: www.BooksByDvorah.com

30 Day Course Creation Challenge for Authors

In the 30 Day Course Creation Challenge for Authors, you have access to a step-by-step guide to creating an online course from your book or area of expertise.

Learn how to:

- Choose the perfect topic for your online course!
- Develop attractive course materials!
- Produce compelling multimedia content!
- Set up your own online classroom, for free!
- Provide interactive components for your students!

Imagine what it would be like to lift the message of your book, right off the pages and into the hearts and minds of

the exact people who are eager to learn from you!

The Course is available at
ReachMoreReaders.com/course

Book available on Amazon and
ActionGuidesForAuthors.com
ISBN: 978-0996743129

30 Day Course Creation Challenge for Authors

D'vorah Lansky, M.Ed.